Andrew Brodie Basics
LET'S DO ADDITION AND SUBTRACTION

FOR AGES 6-7

with over **100** reward stickers

- Over 400 practice questions
- Regular progress tests
- Extra quick-fire questions and handy tips

Published 2016 by Bloomsbury Publishing Plc
50 Bedford Square, London, WC1B 3DP

www.bloomsbury.com

ISBN 978-14729-2620-3

A CIP catalogue for this book is available from the British Library.

10 9 8 7 6 5 4 3 2 1

Printed in China by Leo Paper Products

This book is produced using paper that is made from wood grown in managed, sustainable forests. It is natural, renewable and recyclable. The logging and manufacturing processes conform to the environmental regulations of the country of origin.

To see our full range of titles visit **www.bloomsbury.com**

BLOOMSBURY

Introduction

This is the second in the series of Andrew Brodie *Let's Do Addition and Subtraction* books. The book contains more than 400 mental maths questions, deliberately designed to cover the following key aspects of the 'Number' section of the National Curriculum:

- Number and place value
- Addition and subtraction

Your child will benefit most greatly if you have the opportunity to discuss the questions with them. You may find that your child gains low scores when they first begin to take the tests. Make sure that they don't lose confidence. Instead, encourage them to learn from their mistakes.

The level of difficulty increases gradually throughout the book, but note that some questions are repeated. This is to ensure that pupils have the opportunity to learn vital new facts: they may not know the answer to a particular question the first time they encounter it, but this provides the opportunity for you to help them to learn it for the next time that they come across it. Don't be surprised if they need to practise certain questions many times.

In Year 2, pupils revise a wide range of mathematical vocabulary. In relation to addition, the children need to use expressions such as: 'put together', 'add', 'altogether', 'total' and 'more than'. For subtraction, they use 'take away', 'distance between', 'difference between' and 'less than'. The activities in this book provide opportunities for practising the use of this mathematical language.

It is also important that children learn to understand and use mathematical sentences, appreciating the meanings of the addition, subtraction and equals signs, and relating these to the vocabulary that they have learnt.

Children gain confidence by learning facts that they can use in their future work. With lots of practice they will see their score improve and will learn to find maths both satisfying and enjoyable.

Look out for...

Pippa the Penguin, who provides useful tips and helpful advice.

Brodie's Fast Five, quick-fire questions designed to test your child's mental arithmetic.

Lots of additions

You can use your fingers for some questions if you want to.

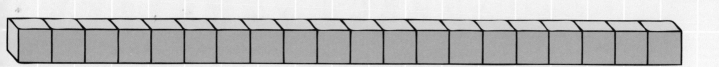

1 $6 + 5 =$ 11

2 4 more than 7 = 11

3 6 more than 8 = 14

4 Add together fourteen and six.

$14 + 6 =$ 20

5 $8 + 3 =$ 11

6 $2 + 9 =$ 11

7 $7 + 8 =$ 15

8 $13 + 6 =$ 19

9 $15 + 3 =$ 18

10 $6 + 11 =$ 17

11 $4 + 9 =$ 13

12 $7 + 6 =$ 13

13 $12 + 5 =$ 17

14 $6 + 13 =$ 19

15 $5 + 15 =$ 20

Magnificent

Brodie's Fast Five

$16 + 2 =$ 18

$23 + 4 =$ 27

$37 + 1 =$ 38

$25 + 3 =$ 28

$30 + 1 =$ 31

3

Lots of subtractions

Remember, you can use your fingers for some questions if you want to.

You can use the number line to help you if you want to.

0 1 2 3 4 5 6 7 8 9 10 11 12 13 14 15 16 17 18 19 20

1 17 – 2 = 15

2 5 less than 17 = 12

3 6 less than 20 = 14

4 Take three away from fifteen.

15 – 3 = 11

5 40 – 1 = 39

6 20 – 11 = 8

7 18 – 6 = 12

8 17 – 8 = 9 ✓

9 19 – 11 = 8 ✓

10 15 – 7 = 8 ✓

11 20 – 6 = 14 ✓

12 16 – 9 = 7 ✓

13 12 – 7 = 5 ✓

14 13 – 8 = 5 ✓

15 15 – 8 = 7 ✓

Keep It Up

Brodie's Fast Five

16 – 2 = 14   14 – 6 = 7

17 – 13 = 2   18 – 2 = 16   20 – 2 = 18

Addition problems

Can you write the addition sentence for each question?

There are six buses and four lorries.
How many vehicles are there altogether?

Here is the addition sentence:

6 + 4 = 10   *There are 10 altogether.*

1 There are eight buses and three cars. How many vehicles are there altogether? Write the addition sentence.

There are 10 altogether

2 There are eleven cars and five vans. How many vehicles are there altogether? Write the addition sentence.

There are 16 altogether

3 There are six lorries and seven vans. How many vehicles are there altogether? Write the addition sentence.

there are 13 altogether

4 There are eight cars and six buses. How many vehicles are there altogether? Write the addition sentence.

there are 14 altogether

Brodie's Fast Five

12 + 12 = *24*   18 + 2 = *20*

17 + 4 = *21*   19 + 3 = *22*   20 + 5 = *25*

5

There were nine cars parked in the car park, but two cars drove away. Seven cars are still parked.

Here is the subtraction sentence:

9 – 2 = 7

SUPER

1 There were eleven cars parked in the car park but four cars drove away. How many cars are still parked? Write the subtraction sentence.

There are 7 cars leged

2 There were nineteen cars parked in the car park but two cars drove away. How many cars are still parked? Write the subtraction sentence.

There are 17 cars tge leged

3 There were fourteen cars parked in the car park but five cars drove away. How many cars are still parked? Write the subtraction sentence.

there are 8 cars leged

4 There were sixteen cars parked in the car park but six cars drove away. How many cars are still parked? Write the subtraction sentence.

then there are 8 cars leged

Brodie's Fast Five

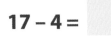

17 – 4 = 13   20 – 5 = 15

16 – 9 = 6   12 – 3 = 9   19 – 8 = 10

Addition and subtraction

Remember to look for the addition sign or the subtraction sign.

This is the addition sign. **+** This is the subtraction sign. **—**

1 $17 + 2 =$ 19

2 5 more than 9 = 14

3 6 less than 6 = 0

Excellent

4 Add together eleven and five. $11 + 5 =$ 16

5 Take three away from nineteen. $19 - 3 =$ 16

6 What is the total of eight and twelve? $8 + 12 =$ 20

7 What is seventeen take away four? $17 - 4 =$ 13

8 Here are seven stars. Draw seven more stars.

How many stars are there altogether? 13 stars

Write the addition sentence about the stars.

$7 + 7 = 13$

9 $20 - 7 =$ 13

10 $20 - 3 =$ 17

Brodie's Fast Five

$19 - 7 =$ 12	$18 - 5 =$ 13	
$17 - 4 =$ 13	$16 - 16 =$ 0	$20 - 5 =$ 15

Addition

1 $6 + 6 =$ 12

2 $8 + 9 =$ 17

3 $5 + 7 =$ 11

4 $15 + 5 =$ 20

5 $19 + 3 =$ 22

Subtraction

6 $18 - 4 =$ 14

7 $19 - 5 =$ 14

8 $20 - 6 =$ 40

9 $16 - 9 =$ 8

10 $25 - 6 =$ 19

11 There are twelve cars and six vans. How many vehicles are there altogether? Write the addition sentence.

$$12 + 6 = 17$$

12 There were eighteen cars parked in the car park but five cars left. How many cars are still parked? Write the subtraction sentence.

$$18 - 5 = 13$$

13 7 more than 9 = 16

14 Add together seventeen and five. $17 + 5 =$ 22

15 Take seven away from twelve. $12 - 7 =$ 5

Adding to find missing numbers

Can you find the missing numbers?

You can use the number line to help you if you want to.

```
0   1   2   3   4   5   6   7   8   9   10   11   12   13   14   15   16   17   18   19   20
|---|---|---|---|---|---|---|---|---|---|----|----|----|----|----|----|----|----|----|----|
```

1　16 + 　4　 = 20

2　3 + 　17　 = 20

3　9 + 　11　 = 20

4　12 + 　32　 = 20

5　4 + 　24　 = 20

6　1 + 　21　 = 20

7　5 + 　25　 = 20

8　8 + 　28　 = 20

9　7 + 　27　 = 20

10　0 + 　20　 = 20

11　6 + 　26　 = 20

12　2 + 　22　 = 20

13　13 + 　31　 = 20

14　18 + 　38　 = 20

15　20 + 　39　 = 20

FAB

Brodie's Fast Five

18 + 6 = 　24　　　12 + 9 = 　21

11 + 11 = 　22　　　13 + 8 = 　2 11　　　17 + 5 = 　22

9

Can you find the missing numbers?

You can use the number line to help you if you want to.

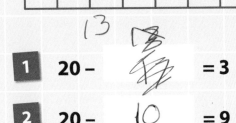

0 1 2 3 4 5 6 7 8 9 10 11 12 13 14 15 16 17 18 19 20

13

1 20 – 13 = 3

2 20 – 10 = 9

3 20 – 19 = 1

4 20 – 9 = 10

5 20 – 15 = 6

6 20 – 13 = 7

7 20 – 30 = 2

8 20 – 14 = 4

20

9 20 – 20 = 0

10 20 – 15 = 5

11 20 – 11 = 8

12 20 – don't = 14   now

13 20 – don't = 17   now

14 20 – don't now = 12

15 20 – don't now = 16

Brodie's Fast Five

23 – 4 = 4

24 – 7 =

24 – 12 =

25 – 15 =

22 – 11 =

10

Let's make seventeen

Look: $10 + 7 = 17$
$7 + 10 = 17$

**Write all the ways of making seventeen by adding whole numbers.
One is done for you.**

9 + 8

7 + 10

θ 10 + 7

17

7 + 10

Write out all the addition bonds that make seventeen. One is done for you.

$16 + 1 = 17$

Brodie's Fast Five

$7 +$ 10 $= 17$ 14 $+ 3 = 17$

$12 +$ 5 $= 17$ 12 $+ 5 = 17$ $9 +$ 8 $= 17$

Let's make eight

Use subtractions to find eight.

Here are some subtractions that make eight.

$$16 - 8 = 8$$
$$12 - 4 = 8$$

Using the numbers below, try to find lots of subtractions that make eight. One is done for you. You can use each number more than once if you want to.

0 1 2 3 4 5 6 7 8 9 10 11 12 13 14 15 16 17 18

16 – 8

12 – 4

16 – 8

8

Write out all the subtraction bonds that you have found to make eight. One is done for you.

12 – 4 = 8

Brodie's Fast Five

20 – ⬚ = 8   ⬚ – 6 = 8

12 – ⬚ = 8   ⬚ – 9 = 8   18 – ⬚ = 8

12

Addition and subtraction

Remember to look for the addition sign or the subtraction sign.

This is the addition sign. ➕   This is the subtraction sign. ➖

1   $18 + 7 =$ **25**

2   6 more than 19 =   **25**

3   1 less than 40 =   **39**

4   Add together eighteen and eight. $18 + 8 =$ **26**

5   Take three away from forty. $40 - 3 =$ **37**

6   What is the total of forty-eight and two? $48 + 2 =$ **50**

7   What is sixteen take away four? $16 - 4 =$ **11**

8   $40 - 6 =$ **34**

9   $40 + 6 =$ **46**

10

How many books are on the top shelf?   **17**   books

How many books are on the lower shelf?   **12**   books

How many more books are there on the top shelf than the lower shelf?

books

Addition

1 13 + ~~7~~ 7 = 20

2 8 + 12 = 20

3 20 + 0 = 20

4 15 + 5 = 20

5 7 + 13 = 20

Subtraction

6 20 – 6 = 14

7 20 – 13 = 6

8 20 – 16 = 11

9 20 – 10 = 9

10 20 – 9 = 10

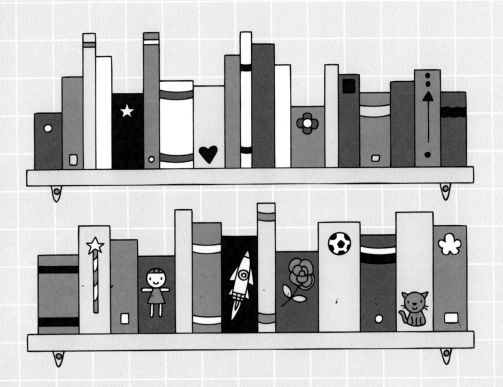

11 How many books are on the top shelf? 19 books

12 How many books are on the lower shelf? 13 books

13 How many more books are there on the top shelf than the lower shelf?

____ books

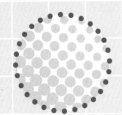

Adding using number lines

Number lines can help a lot with adding.

Look at this number line where we are starting on 16 and adding 13.

Start on 16   Jump 13

0 1 2 3 4 5 6 7 8 9 10 11 12 13 14 15 16 17 18 19 20 21 22 23 24 25 26 27 28 29 30

This is the addition sentence: 16 + 13 = 29

Write the addition sentence for each number line.

14 + 10 23

0 1 2 3 4 5 6 7 8 9 10 11 12 13 14 15 16 17 18 19 20 21 22 23 24 25 26 27 28 29 30

14 + 10 = 23

12

0 1 2 3 4 5 6 7 8 9 10 11 12 13 14 15 16 17 18 19 20 21 22 23 24 25 26 27 28 29 30

15 + 12 = 26

18

0 1 2 3 4 5 6 7 8 9 10 11 12 13 14 15 16 17 18 19 20 21 22 23 24 25 26 27 28 29 30

10 + 18 = 28

0 1 2 3 4 5 6 7 8 9 10 11 12 13 14 15 16 17 18 19 20 21 22 23 24 25 26 27 28 29 30

17 + 13 = 30

0 1 2 3 4 5 6 7 8 9 10 11 12 13 14 15 16 17 18 19 20 21 22 23 24 25 26 27 28 29 30

11 + 10 = 21

Brodie's Fast Five

17 + 7 = 23   18 + 8 = 26

16 + 6 = 21   19 + 9 = 25   20 + 10 = 30

15

Subtracting using number lines

Look at this number line where we are starting on 28 and subtracting 13.

Jump back 13   Start on 28

0 1 2 3 4 5 6 7 8 9 10 11 12 13 14 15 16 17 18 19 20 21 22 23 24 25 26 27 28 29 30

This is the subtraction sentence: 28 − 13 = 15

Write the subtraction sentence for each number line.

0 1 2 3 4 5 6 7 8 9 10 11 12 13 14 15 16 17 18 19 20 21 22 23 24 25 26 27 28 29 30

$$19 - 12^{11} = 7$$

0 1 2 3 4 5 6 7 8 9 10 11 12 13 14 15 16 17 18 19 20 21 22 23 24 25 26 27 28 29 30

$$21 - 8 = 12$$

0 1 2 3 4 5 6 7 8 9 10 11 12 13 14 15 16 17 18 19 20 21 22 23 24 25 26 27 28 29 30

$$26 - 11 = 14$$

0 1 2 3 4 5 6 7 8 9 10 11 12 13 14 15 16 17 18 19 20 21 22 23 24 25 26 27 28 29 30

$$29 - 10 = 18$$

0 1 2 3 4 5 6 7 8 9 10 11 12 13 14 15 16 17 18 19 20 21 22 23 24 25 26 27 28 29 30

$$23 - 7 = 15$$

Brodie's Fast Five

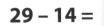

30 − 10 = 19   28 − 21 = 4

25 − 13 = 10   22 − 12 = 8   29 − 14 = 8

Let's make eighteen

There are lots of ways to make eighteen by adding.

Look: 10 + 8 = 18
        8 + 10 = 18

**Write all the ways of making eighteen by adding whole numbers.
One is done for you.**

9 + 9

10 × 8

8 + 10

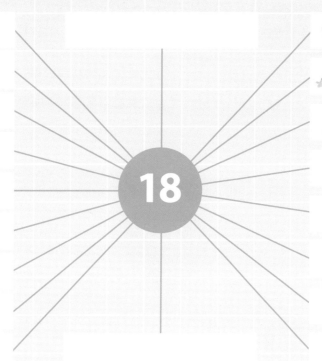

18

Write out all the addition bonds that make eighteen. One is done for you.

17 + 1 = 18

Brodie's Fast Five

6 + 12 = 18   + 13 = 18

12 +   = 18   + 7 = 18   9 +   = 18

Let's make nine

Use subtractions to find nine.

Here are some subtractions that make nine.

$$15 - 6 = 9$$
$$11 - 2 = 9$$

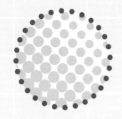

Using the numbers below, try to find lots of subtractions that make nine. One is done for you. You can use each number more than once if you want to.

0 1 2 3 4 5 6 7 8 9 10 11 12 13 14 15 16 17 18 19

15 − 6

11 − 2

9

Write out all the subtraction bonds that you have found to make nine. One is done for you.

12 − 3 = 9

Brodie's Fast Five

| 20 − | = 9 | | − 6 = 9 | |
| 14 − | = 9 | | − 9 = 9 | 22 − | = 9 |

18

Addition and subtraction

Some special words tell you to add and some tell you to subtract.

These are addition words:

put together   add   altogether   total   more than

These are subtraction words:

take away   distance between   difference between   less than

Be careful because 'more than' could be used for subtraction or addition. Look at questions 6 and 7.

1 What is the total of seven and four? $7 + 4 =$

2 How much altogether are seven, eight and nine? $7 + 8 + 9 =$

3 Subtract twelve from twenty-five. $25 - 12 =$

4 Add together twelve and twelve. $12 + 12 =$

5 What is twenty-one take away nine? $21 - 9 =$

6 What is twelve more than twenty? $20 + 12 =$

7 How much more than fifteen is twenty-eight? $28 - 15 =$

8 How much altogether is fourteen and sixteen? $14 + 16 =$

9 How much less than twenty is seventeen? $20 - 17 =$

10 What is twenty minus eleven? $20 - 11 =$

11 Twenty-two subtract seven. $22 - 7 =$

12 What is the total of eighteen and eleven? $18 + 11 =$

13 What is the difference between forty and twenty? $40 - 20 =$

14 Find the total of eleven and twelve. $11 + 12 =$

15 Eighteen minus six. $18 - 6 =$

Brodie's Fast Five

$19 - 4 =$ $17 - 3 =$

$15 - 7 =$ $16 - 9 =$ $14 - 9 =$

Addition   Write the addition sentence for each number line.

1 0 1 2 3 4 5 6 7 8 9 10 11 12 13 14 15 16 17 18 19 20 21 22 23 24 25 26 27 28 29 30

2 0 1 2 3 4 5 6 7 8 9 10 11 12 13 14 15 16 17 18 19 20 21 22 23 24 25 26 27 28 29 30

3 0 1 2 3 4 5 6 7 8 9 10 11 12 13 14 15 16 17 18 19 20 21 22 23 24 25 26 27 28 29 30

Subtraction   Write the subtraction sentence for each number line.

4 0 1 2 3 4 5 6 7 8 9 10 11 12 13 14 15 16 17 18 19 20 21 22 23 24 25 26 27 28 29 30

5 0 1 2 3 4 5 6 7 8 9 10 11 12 13 14 15 16 17 18 19 20 21 22 23 24 25 26 27 28 29 30

6 0 1 2 3 4 5 6 7 8 9 10 11 12 13 14 15 16 17 18 19 20 21 22 23 24 25 26 27 28 29 30

7 What is nine more than twenty?

8 How much more than thirteen is twenty-four?

9 How much altogether is fifteen and five?

10 How much less than thirty is nineteen?

11 What is twenty minus six?

12 Twenty-two subtract eight.

13 What is the total of nine and eleven?

14 What is the difference between fifty and twenty?

15 Find the total of six and twelve.

16 Twenty-one minus six.

Addition bonds to 20

Ask someone to time how quickly you answer the two sets of questions.

A

1	6 + 7 =	13
2	4 + 9 =	13
3	6 + 9 =	15
4	8 + 9 =	17
5	6 + 5 =	11
6	14 + 3 =	17
7	16 + 4 =	20
8	8 + 6 =	14
9	5 + 7 =	12
10	12 + 5 =	17

B

1	5 + 7 =	12
2	9 + 9 =	18
3	3 + 7 =	10
4	12 + 6 =	18
5	4 + 7 =	11
6	13 + 6 =	19
7	6 + 6 =	12
8	8 + 8 =	16
9	11 + 7 =	18
10	4 + 9 =	13

Brodie's Fast Five

7 +   = 18   + 5 = 18

14 +   = 18   + 9 = 18   6 +   = 18

21

Subtraction bonds to 20

Ask someone to time how quickly you answer the two sets of questions.

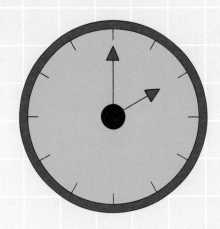

A

1	16 − 7 =	8
2	14 − 9 =	4
3	18 − 3 =	15
4	18 − 8 =	10
5	20 − 12 =	7
6	15 − 7 =	7
7	16 − 4 =	12
8	17 − 8 =	8
9	19 − 7 =	11
10	12 − 8 =	4

B

1	16 − 13 =	2
2	17 − 12 =	4
3	13 − 8 =	5
4	14 − 6 =	7
5	16 − 9 =	7
6	18 − 11 =	6
7	11 − 5 =	6
8	12 − 9 =	3
9	15 − 8 =	6
10	20 − 9 =	10

Brodie's Fast Five

20 − [ ] = 4   [ ] − 7 = 13

14 − [ ] = 3   [ ] − 13 = 2   16 − [ ] = 1

22

Let's make nineteen

There are lots of ways to make nineteen by adding.

Look: $10 + 9 = 19$
$9 + 10 = 19$

Write all the ways of making nineteen by adding whole numbers.
One is done for you.

$10 + 9$

$9 + 10$

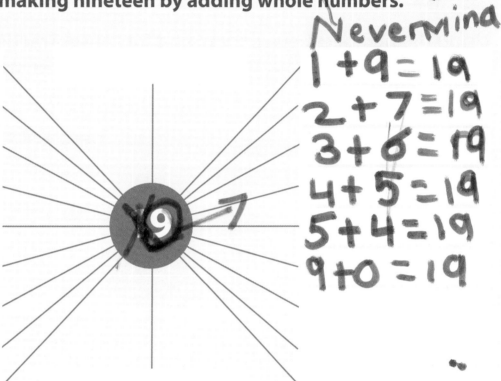

Nevermind
$1 + 9 = 19$
$2 + 7 = 19$
$3 + 6 = 19$
$4 + 5 = 19$
$5 + 4 = 19$
$9 + 0 = 19$

Write out all the addition bonds that make nineteen. One is done for you.

$18 + 1 = 19$ $10 + 9$

Brodie's Fast Five

$6 + = 19$	$ + 13 = 19$	
$12 + = 19$	$ + 7 = 19$	$9 + = 19$

Let's make ten

Use subtractions to find ten.

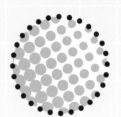

Here are some subtractions that make ten.

$$15 - 5 = 10$$
$$19 - 9 = 10$$

Using the numbers below, try to find lots of subtractions that make ten. One is done for you. You can use each number more than once if you want to.

0 1 2 3 4 5 6 7 8 9 10 11 12 13 14 15 16 17 18 19 20

15 – 5

19 – 9 =

5 – 15 =

19 – 19 =

12 – 2

2 – 12

10

Write out all the subtraction bonds that you have found to make ten. One is done for you.

12 – 2 = 10

Brodie's Fast Five

| 20 – ___ = 10 | ___ – 6 = 10 |
| 13 – ___ = 10 | ___ – 8 = 10   25 – ___ = 10 |

Addition and subtraction

Do you know that additions and subtractions are related to each other?

Look at four calculations using the numbers 4, 6 and 10.

Additions:

$6 + 4 = 10$ $4 + 6 = 10$

Subtractions:

$10 - 6 = 4$ $10 - 4 = 6$

1 Write four calculations using the numbers 3, 4 and 7.

Additions:

Subtractions:

2 Write four calculations using the numbers 3, 6 and 9.

Additions:

Subtractions:

Brodie's Fast Five

$16 - 4 =$ $10 - 3 =$

$20 - 2 =$ $20 - 12 =$ $15 - 8 =$

Look carefully at the addition or subtraction sign in each question.
How quickly can you answer the questions?

1 7 + 8 =

2 12 – 6 =

3 10 + 4 =

4 15 – 9 =

5 7 + 8 =

6 20 – 9 =

7 12 + 6 =

8 17 – 9 =

9 18 + 2 =

10 20 – 16 =

11 8 + 8 =

12 15 – 7 =

13 10 + 10 =

14 14 – 6 =

15 7 + 9 =

16 20 – 11 =

17 16 + 4 =

18 17 – 8 =

19 14 + 6 =

20 20 – 3 =

21 Write four calculations using the numbers 5, 6 and 11.

Additions:

Subtractions:

22 Write four calculations using the numbers 2, 7 and 9.

Additions:

Subtractions:

Adding multiples of ten

Ask someone to time how quickly you answer the two sets of questions.

Look carefully at these two calculations for adding multiples of ten:

$$40 + 8 = 48$$
$$7 + 60 = 67$$

What do you notice about them?
Can you work out the following similar calculations?

A

1. $60 + 7 =$
2. $4 + 90 =$
3. $60 + 9 =$
4. $8 + 90 =$
5. $60 + 5 =$
6. $4 + 30 =$
7. $50 + 4 =$
8. $8 + 70 =$
9. $50 + 7 =$
10. $80 + 5 =$

B

1. $5 + 70 =$
2. $90 + 9 =$
3. $3 + 70 =$
4. $20 + 6 =$
5. $4 + 70 =$
6. $30 + 6 =$
7. $6 + 60 =$
8. $80 + 8 =$
9. $10 + 70 =$
10. $40 + 9 =$

Brodie's Fast Five

$70 + \quad = 78$ $\quad + 7 = 57$

$60 + \quad = 63$ $\quad + 90 = 98$ $6 + \quad = 46$

Subtracting from multiples of ten

Look at the calculations carefully.

Look at these calculations:

10 – 7 = 3

20 – 7 = 13

30 – 7 = 23

40 – 7 = 33

50 – 7 = 43

60 – 7 = 53

70 – 7 = 63

80 – 7 = 73

90 – 7 = 83

100 – 7 = 93

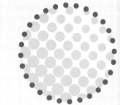

Now try these.

1	10 – 6 =	11	10 – 2 =
2	20 – 6 =	12	20 – 2 =
3	30 – 6 =	13	30 – 2 =
4	40 – 6 =	14	40 – 2 =
5	50 – 6 =	15	50 – 2 =
6	60 – 6 =	16	60 – 2 =
7	70 – 6 =	17	70 – 2 =
8	80 – 6 =	18	80 – 2 =
9	90 – 6 =	19	90 – 2 =
10	100 – 6 =	20	100 – 2 =

Brodie's Fast Five

10 – 4 =

10 – 5 =

10 – 9 =

10 – 3 =

10 – 8 =

Let's make twenty

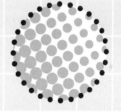
There are lots of ways to make twenty by adding.

Look:
$$11 + 9 = 20$$
$$9 + 11 = 20$$

Write all the ways of making twenty by adding whole numbers.
One is done for you.

10 + 10

11 + 9
9 + 11
10 + 11
16 + 4
15 + 3
3 + 15
4 + 16
18 + 2
17 + 3

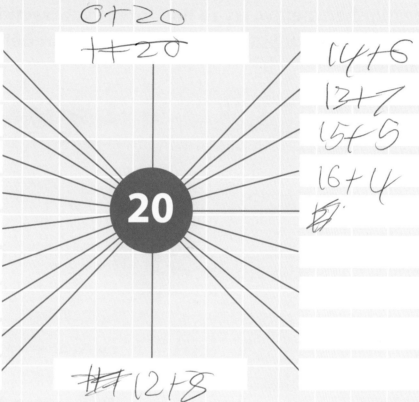

0 + 20
1 + 20

14 + 6
13 + 7
15 + 5
16 + 4

12 + 8

Write out all the addition bonds that make twenty. One is done for you.

19 + 1 = 20

Brodie's Fast Five

6 +   = 20   + 13 = 20

12 +   = 20   + 7 = 20   9 +   = 20

29

Let's make eleven

Use subtractions to find eleven.

Here are some subtractions that make eleven.

$20 - 9 = 11$
$19 - 8 = 11$

Using the numbers below, try to find lots of subtractions that make eleven. One is done for you. You can use each number more than once if you want to.

0 1 2 3 4 5 6 7 8 9 10 11 12 13 14 15 16 17 18 19 20 21

15 – 4

2 0 → 9
19 ~ 8
8 ~ 19
2Ø 9~20

12 – 1

9 ≠ 2
8 ≠ 3
≠4 14 – 3
12 13 = 2 15 – 4

(11)

Write out all the subtraction bonds that you have found to make eleven. One is done for you.

$12 - 1 = 11$

Brodie's Fast Five

20 – ___ = 11	___ – 6 = 11	
13 – ___ = 11	___ – 8 = 11	22 – ___ = 11

30

Addition and subtraction

Do you remember how additions and subtractions are related to each other?

Look at these four calculations using the numbers 3, 17 and 20.

Additions:

3 + 17 = 20   17 + 3 = 20

Subtractions:

20 − 17 = 3   20 − 3 = 17

1 **Write four calculations using the numbers 5, 15 and 20.**

Additions:

Subtractions:

2 **Write four calculations using the numbers 7, 8 and 15.**

Additions:

Subtractions:

Brodie's Fast Five

64 − 4 =   83 − 3 =

92 − 2 =   76 − 70 =   95 − 90 =

Look carefully at the addition or subtraction sign in each question.
How quickly can you answer the questions?

1	10 – 5 =		11	10 – 3 =	1
2	20 – 5 =		12	20 – 3 =	
3	30 – 5 =		13	30 – 3 =	
4	40 – 5 =		14	40 – 3 =	
5	50 – 5 =		15	50 – 3 =	
6	60 – 5 =		16	60 – 3 =	
7	70 – 5 =		17	70 – 3 =	
8	80 – 5 =		18	80 – 3 =	
9	90 – 5 =		19	90 – 3 =	
10	100 – 5 =		20	100 – 3 =	

21 Write four calculations using the numbers 6, 13 and 19.

Additions:

Subtractions:

22 Write four calculations using the numbers 8, 5 and 13.

Additions:

Subtractions:

Adding two-digit numbers and units

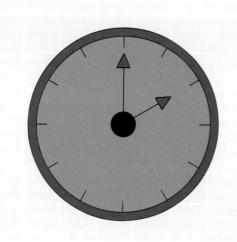

Ask someone to time how quickly you answer the two sets of questions.

A

1. 26 + 3 =
2. 44 + 4 =
3. 52 + 7 =
4. 31 + 9 =
5. 76 + 5 =
6. 84 + 3 =
7. 67 + 4 =
8. 92 + 7 =
9. 65 + 7 =
10. 88 + 5 =

B

1. 35 + 7 =
2. 89 + 9 =
3. 63 + 7 =
4. 58 + 6 =
5. 34 + 7 =
6. 47 + 6 =
7. 59 + 6 =
8. 28 + 8 =
9. 33 + 4 =
10. 94 + 9 =

Brodie's Fast Five

7 + ___ = 39   ___ + 5 = 47

4 + ___ = 56   ___ + 9 = 72   6 + ___ = 88

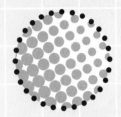

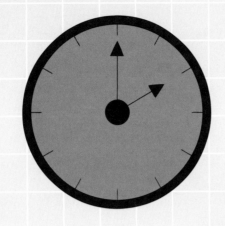

Ask someone to time how quickly you answer the two sets of questions.

A

1 39 – 6 =

2 58 – 7 =

3 79 – 3 =

4 99 – 4 =

5 67 – 5 =

6 48 – 7 =

7 56 – 6 =

8 85 – 8 =

9 92 – 5 =

10 74 – 6 =

B

1 68 – 2 =

2 37 – 2 =

3 42 – 2 =

4 75 – 2 =

5 91 – 2 =

6 53 – 2 =

7 84 – 2 =

8 55 – 2 =

9 95 – 2 =

10 23 – 2 =

Brodie's Fast Five

69 – ____ = 62   47 – ____ = 43

88 – ____ = 84   52 – ____ = 47   91 – ____ = 85

Adding two-digit numbers and tens

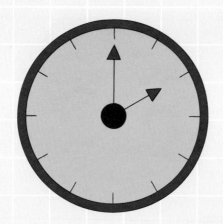

It's easy to add multiples of ten to other two-digit numbers.

A

1. 26 + 40 =
2. 44 + 30 =
3. 52 + 20 =
4. 37 + 50 =
5. 48 + 30 =
6. 25 + 70 =
7. 18 + 80 =
8. 32 + 60 =
9. 21 + 60 =
10. 38 + 40 =

B

1. 20 + 78 =
2. 50 + 49 =
3. 60 + 27 =
4. 30 + 46 =
5. 70 + 17 =
6. 40 + 23 =
7. 50 + 32 =
8. 80 + 28 =
9. 70 + 36 =
10. 90 + 15 =

Brodie's Fast Five

27 + [ ] = 67   [ ] + 30 = 59

43 + [ ] = 93   [ ] + 39 = 79   61 + [ ] = 81

It's easy to subtract multiples of ten from other two-digit numbers.

But it's harder to subtract other two-digit numbers from multiples of ten.

You may find the number line helpful.

0 5 10 15 20 25 30 35 40 45 50 55 60 65 70 75 80 85 90 95 100

1	87 – 20 =		**11**	90 – 24 =
2	93 – 40 =		**12**	40 – 17 =
3	76 – 50 =		**13**	80 – 53 =
4	34 – 20 =		**14**	60 – 19 =
5	59 – 30 =		**15**	30 – 18 =
6	72 – 40 =		**16**	70 – 47 =
7	95 – 60 =		**17**	90 – 45 =
8	48 – 20 =		**18**	100 – 33 =
9	61 – 30 =		**19**	80 – 39 =
10	38 – 10 =		**20**	60 – 42 =

Brodie's Fast Five

49 – ___ = 19   ___ – 40 = 59

83 – ___ = 53   ___ – 42 = 8   100 – ___ = 81

Do you remember how additions and subtractions are related to each other?

Look at the four calculations using the numbers 23, 17 and 40.

Additions:

$$23 + 17 = 40 \qquad 17 + 23 = 40$$

Subtractions:

$$40 - 17 = 23 \qquad 40 - 23 = 17$$

1 Write four calculations using the numbers 36, 24 and 60.

Additions:

Subtractions:

2 Write four calculations using the numbers 48, 32 and 80.

Additions:

Subtractions:

Brodie's Fast Five

$$64 - 40 = \qquad 87 - 30 =$$

$$92 - 20 = \qquad 76 - 50 = \qquad 95 - 60 =$$

37

questions as quickly as you can.

1	34 + 3 =	
2	53 + 4 =	
3	81 + 7 =	
4	51 + 9 =	
5	88 + 5 =	
6	59 – 7 =	
7	76 – 6 =	
8	93 – 8 =	
9	51 – 5 =	
10	34 – 6 =	

11	20 + 47 =	
12	50 + 32 =	
13	60 + 39 =	
14	30 + 56 =	
15	70 + 23 =	
16	82 – 30 =	
17	76 – 40 =	
18	90 – 33 =	
19	50 – 29 =	
20	60 – 17 =	

21 Write four calculations using the numbers 23, 37 and 60.

Additions:

Subtractions:

22 Write four calculations using the numbers 46, 24 and 70.

Additions:

Subtractions:

Addition in columns explanation page

Read the explanation on this page very carefully.

Look at these numbers:

4   6   2   3

There are   **There are**   **There are**   **There are**
four tens.   **six units.**   **two tens.**   **three units.**

To add 64 and 31, we can write them one above the other. We say that the 4 and the 1 are in the 'units' column. The 6 and the 3 are in the 'tens' column.

```
    4  6            4  6            4  6
 +  2  3         +  2  3         +  2  3
 _____       _____       _____
                       9            6  9
```

We add the   **Then we add the tens to**
units first.   **get the final answer.**

Sometimes there are enough units to make an extra ten.

```
    4  7            4  7            4  7
 +  2  5         +  2  5         +  2  5
 _____       _____       _____
                       2            7  2
                    1               1
```

7 units + 5 units is enough   **Then we add all the tens,**
to make a ten and 2 units   **including the extra 1 to get**
because 7 + 5 = 12.   **the final answer.**

Addition in columns

It's your chance to write additions in columns.

1 52 + 26

```
      5  2
  +   2  6
  _____
      7  8
```

2 63 + 14

3 34 + 25

4 46 + 31

5 58 + 31

6 67 + 25

7 49 + 35

8 38 + 38

9 69 + 27

10 45 + 45

Brodie's Fast Five

46 + 3 =   46 + 13 =

46 + 23 =   46 + 33 =   46 + 43 =

Read the explanation on this page very carefully.

Look at these numbers:

7   8   3   5

There are   There are   There are   There are
seven tens.   eight units.   three tens.   five units.

To subtract 35 from 78 we can write the 78 above the 35. We say that the 8 and the 5 are in the units column. The 7 and the 3 are in the tens column.

```
   7  8           7  8           7  8
-  3  5        -  3  5        -  3  5
_____       _____       _____
                     3           4  3
```

We subtract the 5 units   Then we subtract the 3
from the 8 units first.   tens from the 7 tens.

Sometimes there are not enough units in the top number. So we break one of the tens into ten extra units then do the subtraction.

We use one of the 6 tens to   Then we subtract the
make ten extra units so now   tens to get the final
we have 13 units and can   answer.
subtract the 8 units

```
   6  3          5  1          5  1
               6  3          6  3
-  2  8        -  2  8        -  2  8
_____       _____       _____
   3  5           3  5           3  5
```

41

Subtraction in columns

It's your chance to write subtractions in columns.

1 68 – 35

```
    6   8
–   3   5
─────────
    3   3
```

2 79 – 42

3 97 – 56

4 84 – 21

5 56 – 34

6 72 – 47

7 81 – 58

8 93 – 38

9 80 – 32

10 96 – 44

Brodie's Fast Five

69 – 2 =   69 – 12 =

69 – 22 =   69 – 32 =   69 – 42 =

42

Addition and subtraction

Write the additions and subtractions in columns.

1   48 – 25

6   58 + 36

2   34 + 25

7   61 – 29

3   79 – 34

8   56 + 29

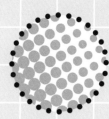

4   43 + 36

9   80 – 36

5   52 – 36

10   67 + 33

Brodie's Fast Five

57 – 3 =   57 – 13 =

57 – 23 =   57 – 33 =   57 – 43 =

1 84 – 37

6 37 + 37

2 67 + 29

7 99 – 54

3 72 – 48

8 58 + 37

4 42 + 36

9 90 – 45

5 80 – 36

10 71 + 29

11 **Write the two subtraction sentences to go with each addition sentence.**

69 + 31 = 100   46 + 36 = 82   57 + 44 = 101

ANSWERS

Page 3 • Lots of additions

1. 6 + 5 = 11
2. 4 more than 7 = 11
3. 6 more than 8 = 14
4. 14 + 6 = 20
5. 8 + 3 = 11
6. 2 + 9 = 11
7. 7 + 8 = 15
8. 13 + 6 = 19
9. 15 + 3 = 18
10. 6 + 11 = 17
11. 4 + 9 = 13
12. 7 + 6 = 13
13. 12 + 5 = 17
14. 6 + 13 = 19
15. 5 + 15 = 20

Brodie's Fast Five

16 + 2 = 18
23 + 4 = 27
37 + 1 = 38
25 + 3 = 28
30 + 1 = 31

Page 4 • Lots of subtractions

1. 17 – 2 = 15
2. 5 less than 17 = 12
3. 6 less than 20 = 14
4. 15 – 3 = 12
5. 40 – 1 = 39
6. 20 – 11 = 9
7. 18 – 6 = 12
8. 17 – 8 = 9
9. 19 – 11 = 8
10. 15 – 7 = 8
11. 20 – 6 = 14
12. 16 – 9 = 7
13. 12 – 7 = 5
14. 13 – 8 = 5
15. 15 – 8 = 7

Brodie's Fast Five

16 – 2 = 14
14 – 6 = 8
17 – 13 = 4
18 – 2 = 16
20 – 2 = 18

Page 5 • Addition problems

1. 8 + 3 = 11
2. 11 + 5 = 16
3. 6 + 7 = 13
4. 8 + 6 = 14

Brodie's Fast Five

12 + 12 = 24
18 + 2 = 20
17 + 4 = 21
19 + 3 = 22
20 + 5 = 25

Page 6 • Subtraction problems

1. 11 – 4 = 7
2. 19 – 2 = 17
3. 14 – 5 = 9
4. 16 – 6 = 10

Brodie's Fast Five

17 – 4 = 13
20 – 5 = 15
16 – 9 = 7
12 – 3 = 9
19 – 8 = 11

Page 7 • Addition and subtraction

1. 17 + 2 = 19
2. 5 more than 9 = 14
3. 6 less than 6 = 0
4. 11 + 5 = 16
5. 19 – 3 = 16
6. 8 + 12 = 20
7. 17 – 4 = 13
8. 14 stars
   7 + 7 = 14
9. 20 – 7 = 13
10. 20 – 3 = 17

Brodie's Fast Five

19 – 7 = 12
18 – 5 = 13
17 – 4 = 13
16 – 16 = 0
20 – 5 = 15

Page 8 • Progress Test 1

Addition
1. 6 + 6 = 12
2. 8 + 9 = 17
3. 5 + 7 = 12
4. 15 + 5 = 20
5. 19 + 3 = 22

Subtraction
6. 18 – 4 = 14
7. 19 – 5 = 14
8. 20 – 6 = 14
9. 16 – 9 = 7
10. 25 – 6 = 19

11. 12 + 6 = 18
12. 18 – 5 = 13
13. 7 more than 9 = 16
14. 17 + 5 = 22
15. 12 – 7 = 5

Page 9 • Adding to find missing numbers

1. 16 + 4 = 20
2. 3 + 17 = 20
3. 9 + 11 = 20
4. 12 + 8 = 20
5. 4 + 16 = 20
6. 1 + 19 = 20
7. 5 + 15 = 20
8. 8 + 12 = 20
9. 7 + 13 = 20
10. 0 + 20 = 20

11. 6 + 14 = 20
12. 2 + 18 = 20
13. 13 + 7 = 20
14. 18 + 2 = 20
15. 20 + 0 = 20

Brodie's Fast Five

18 + 6 = 24
12 + 9 = 21
11 + 11 = 22
13 + 8 = 21
17 + 5 = 22

Page 10 • Subtracting to find missing numbers

1. 20 – 17 = 3
2. 20 – 11 = 9
3. 20 – 19 = 1
4. 20 – 10 = 10
5. 20 – 14 = 6
6. 20 – 13 = 7
7. 20 – 18 = 2
8. 20 – 16 = 4
9. 20 – 20 = 0
10. 20 – 15 = 5
11. 20 – 12 = 8
12. 20 – 6 = 14
13. 20 – 3 = 17
14. 20 – 8 = 12
15. 20 – 4 = 16

Brodie's Fast Five

23 – 4 = 19
24 – 7 = 17
24 – 12 = 12
25 – 15 = 10
22 – 11 = 11

Page 11 • Let's make seventeen

0 + 17
17 + 0
1 + 16
16 + 1
2 + 15
15 + 2
3 + 14
14 + 3
4 + 13
13 + 4
5 + 12
12 + 5
6 + 11
11 + 6
7 + 10
10 + 7
8 + 9
9 + 8

0 + 17 = 17
17 + 0 = 17
1 + 16 = 17
16 + 1 = 17
2 + 15 = 17
15 + 2 = 17
3 + 14 = 17
14 + 3 = 17
4 + 13 = 17
13 + 4 = 17

5 + 12 = 17
12 + 5 = 17
6 + 11 = 17
11 + 6 = 17
7 + 10 = 17
10 + 7 = 17
8 + 9 = 17
9 + 8 = 17

Brodie's Fast Five

7 + 10 = 17
14 + 3 = 17
12 + 5 = 17
12 + 5 = 17
9 + 8 = 17

Page 12 • Let's make eight

18 – 10
17 – 9
16 – 8
15 – 7
14 – 6
13 – 5
12 – 4
11 – 3
10 – 2
9 – 1
8 – 0

18 – 10 = 8
17 – 9 = 8
16 – 8 = 8
15 – 7 = 8
14 – 6 = 8
13 – 5 = 8
12 – 4 = 8
11 – 3 = 8
10 – 2 = 8
9 – 1 = 8
8 – 0 = 8

Brodie's Fast Five

20 – 12 = 8
14 – 6 = 8
12 – 4 = 8
17 – 9 = 8
18 – 10 = 8

Page 13 • Addition and subtraction

1. 18 + 7 = 25
2. 6 more than 19 = 25
3. 1 less than 40 = 39
4. 18 + 8 = 26
5. 40 – 3 = 37
6. 48 + 2 = 50
7. 16 – 4 = 12
8. 40 – 6 = 34
9. 40 + 6 = 46
10. 17 books
11. 12 books
12. 5 books

Page 14 • Progress Test 2

Addition
1. $13 + 7 = 20$
2. $8 + 12 = 20$
3. $20 + 0 = 20$
4. $15 + 5 = 20$
5. $7 + 13 = 20$

Subtraction
6. $20 - 6 = 14$
7. $20 - 14 = 6$
8. $20 - 9 = 11$
9. $20 - 11 = 9$
10. $20 - 10 = 10$

11. 19 books
12. 13 books
13. 6 books

Page 15 • Adding using number lines

$14 + 9 = 23$
$15 + 11 = 26$
$10 + 18 = 28$
$17 + 13 = 30$
$11 + 10 = 21$

Brodie's Fast Five

$17 + 7 = 24$
$18 + 8 = 26$
$16 + 6 = 22$
$19 + 9 = 28$
$20 + 10 = 30$

Page 16 • Subtracting using number lines

$21 - 9 = 12$
$26 - 12 = 14$
$29 - 11 = 18$
$23 - 8 = 15$

Brodie's Fast Five

$30 - 10 = 20$
$28 - 21 = 7$
$25 - 13 = 12$
$22 - 12 = 10$
$29 - 14 = 15$

Page 17 • Let's make eighteen

$0 + 18$
$18 + 0$
$1 + 17$
$17 + 1$
$2 + 16$
$16 + 2$
$3 + 15$
$15 + 3$
$4 + 14$
$14 + 4$
$5 + 13$
$13 + 5$
$6 + 12$
$12 + 6$
$7 + 11$
$11 + 7$
$8 + 10$
$10 + 8$
$9 + 9$

$0 + 18 = 18$
$18 + 0 = 18$
$1 + 17 = 18$
$17 + 1 = 18$
$2 + 16 = 18$
$16 + 2 = 18$
$3 + 15 = 18$
$15 + 3 = 18$
$4 + 14 = 18$
$14 + 4 = 18$
$5 + 13 = 18$
$13 + 5 = 18$
$6 + 12 = 18$
$12 + 6 = 18$
$7 + 11 = 18$
$11 + 7 = 18$
$8 + 10 = 18$
$10 + 8 = 18$
$9 + 9 = 18$

Brodie's Fast Five

$6 + 12 = 18$
$5 + 13 = 18$
$12 + 6 = 18$
$11 + 7 = 18$
$9 + 9 = 18$

Page 18 • Let's make nine

$19 - 10$
$18 - 9$
$17 - 8$
$16 - 7$
$15 - 6$
$14 - 5$
$13 - 4$
$12 - 3$
$11 - 2$
$10 - 1$
$9 - 0$

$19 - 10 = 9$
$18 - 9 = 9$
$17 - 8 = 9$
$16 - 7 = 9$
$15 - 6 = 9$
$14 - 5 = 9$
$13 - 4 = 9$
$12 - 3 = 9$
$11 - 2 = 9$
$10 - 1 = 9$
$9 - 0 = 9$

Brodie's Fast Five

$20 - 11 = 9$
$15 - 6 = 9$
$14 - 5 = 9$
$18 - 9 = 9$
$22 - 13 = 9$

Page 19 • Addition and subtraction

1. $7 + 4 = 11$
2. $7 + 8 + 9 = 24$
3. $25 - 12 = 13$
4. $12 + 12 = 24$
5. $21 - 9 = 12$
6. $20 + 12 = 32$
7. $28 - 15 = 13$
8. $14 + 16 = 30$
9. $20 - 17 = 3$
10. $20 - 11 = 9$
11. $22 - 7 = 15$
12. $18 + 11 = 29$
13. $40 - 20 = 20$
14. $11 + 12 = 23$
15. $18 - 6 = 12$

Brodie's Fast Five

$19 - 4 = 15$
$17 - 3 = 14$
$15 - 7 = 8$
$16 - 9 = 7$
$14 - 9 = 5$

Page 20 • Progress Test 3

Addition
1. $16 + 7 = 23$
2. $12 + 16 = 28$
3. $15 + 9 = 24$

Subtraction
4. $22 - 15 = 7$
5. $19 - 7 = 12$
6. $26 - 15 = 11$

7. $20 + 9 = 29$
8. $24 - 13 = 11$
9. $15 + 5 = 20$
10. $30 - 19 = 11$
11. $20 - 6 = 14$
12. $22 - 8 = 14$
13. $9 + 11 = 20$
14. $50 - 20 = 30$
15. $6 + 12 = 18$
16. $21 - 6 = 15$

Page 21 • Addition bonds to 20

Set A
1. $6 + 7 = 13$
2. $4 + 9 = 13$
3. $6 + 9 = 15$
4. $8 + 9 = 17$
5. $6 + 5 = 11$
6. $14 + 3 = 17$
7. $16 + 4 = 20$
8. $8 + 6 = 14$
9. $5 + 7 = 12$
10. $12 + 5 = 17$

Set B
1. $5 + 7 = 12$
2. $9 + 9 = 18$
3. $3 + 7 = 10$
4. $12 + 6 = 18$
5. $4 + 7 = 11$
6. $13 + 6 = 19$
7. $6 + 6 = 12$
8. $8 + 8 = 16$
9. $11 + 7 = 18$
10. $4 + 9 = 13$

Brodie's Fast Five

$7 + 11 = 18$
$13 + 5 = 18$
$14 + 4 = 18$
$9 + 9 = 18$
$6 + 12 = 18$

Page 22 • Subtraction bonds to 20

Set A
1. $16 - 7 = 9$
2. $14 - 9 = 5$
3. $18 - 3 = 15$
4. $18 - 8 = 10$
5. $20 - 12 = 8$
6. $15 - 7 = 8$
7. $16 - 4 = 12$
8. $17 - 8 = 9$
9. $19 - 7 = 12$
10. $12 - 8 = 4$

Set B
1. $16 - 13 = 3$
2. $17 - 12 = 5$
3. $13 - 8 = 5$
4. $14 - 6 = 8$
5. $16 - 9 = 7$
6. $18 - 11 = 7$
7. $11 - 5 = 6$
8. $12 - 9 = 3$
9. $15 - 8 = 7$
10. $20 - 9 = 11$

Brodie's Fast Five

$20 - 16 = 4$
$20 - 7 = 13$
$14 - 11 = 3$
$15 - 13 = 2$
$16 - 15 = 1$

Page 23 • Let's make nineteen

$0 + 19$
$19 + 0$
$1 + 18$
$18 + 1$
$2 + 17$
$17 + 2$
$3 + 16$
$16 + 3$
$4 + 15$
$15 + 4$
$5 + 14$
$14 + 5$
$6 + 13$
$13 + 6$
$7 + 12$
$12 + 7$
$8 + 11$
$11 + 8$
$9 + 10$
$10 + 9$

$0 + 19 = 19$
$19 + 0 = 19$
$1 + 18 = 19$
$18 + 1 = 19$
$2 + 17 = 19$
$17 + 2 = 19$
$3 + 16 = 19$
$16 + 3 = 19$
$4 + 15 = 19$
$15 + 4 = 19$
$5 + 14 = 19$
$14 + 5 = 19$
$6 + 13 = 19$
$13 + 6 = 19$
$7 + 12 = 19$
$12 + 7 = 19$
$8 + 11 = 19$
$11 + 8 = 19$
$9 + 10 = 19$
$10 + 9 = 19$

Brodie's Fast Five

$6 + 13 = 19$
$6 + 13 = 19$
$12 + 7 = 19$
$12 + 7 = 19$
$9 + 10 = 19$

Page 24 • Let's make ten

20 – 10
19 – 9
18 – 8
17 – 7
16 – 6
15 – 5
14 – 4
13 – 3
12 – 2
11 – 1
10 – 0

20 – 10 = 10
19 – 9 = 10
18 – 8 = 10
17 – 7 = 10
16 – 6 = 10
15 – 5 = 10
14 – 4 = 10
13 – 3 = 10
12 – 2 = 10
11 – 1 = 10
10 – 0 = 10

Brodie's Fast Five

20 – 10 = 10
16 – 6 = 10
13 – 3 = 10
18 – 8 = 10
25 – 15 = 10

Page 25 • Addition and subtraction

1. Additions:
   3 + 4 = 7   4 + 3 = 7
   Subtractions:
   7 – 4 = 3   7 – 3 = 4
2. Additions:
   3 + 6 = 9   6 + 3 = 9
   Subtractions:
   9 – 6 = 3   9 – 3 = 6

Brodie's Fast Five

16 – 4 = 12
10 – 3 = 7
20 – 2 = 18
20 – 12 = 8
15 – 8 = 7

Page 26 • Progress Test 4

1. 7 + 8 = 15
2. 12 – 6 = 6
3. 10 + 4 = 14
4. 15 – 9 = 6
5. 7 + 8 = 15
6. 20 – 9 = 11
7. 12 + 6 = 18
8. 17 – 9 = 8
9. 18 + 2 = 20
10. 20 – 16 = 4
11. 8 + 8 = 16
12. 15 – 7 = 8
13. 10 + 10 = 20
14. 14 – 6 = 8
15. 7 + 9 = 16
16. 20 – 11 = 9
17. 16 + 4 = 20
18. 17 – 8 = 9
19. 14 + 6 = 20
20. 20 – 3 = 17

21. Additions:
    5 + 6 = 11   6 + 5 = 11
    Subtractions:
    11 – 6 = 5   11 – 5 = 6
22. Additions:
    2 + 7 = 9   7 + 2 = 9
    Subtractions:
    9 – 7 = 2   9 – 2 = 7

Page 27 • Adding multiples of ten

Set A
1. 60 + 7 = 67
2. 4 + 90 = 94
3. 60 + 9 = 69
4. 8 + 90 = 98
5. 60 + 5 = 65
6. 4 + 30 = 34
7. 50 + 4 = 54
8. 8 + 70 = 78
9. 50 + 7 = 57
10. 80 + 5 = 85

Set B
1. 5 + 70 = 75
2. 90 + 9 = 99
3. 3 + 70 = 73
4. 20 + 6 = 26
5. 4 + 70 = 74
6. 30 + 6 = 36
7. 6 + 60 = 66
8. 80 + 8 = 88
9. 11 + 70 = 81
10. 40 + 9 = 49

Brodie's Fast Five

70 + 8 = 78
50 + 7 = 57
60 + 3 = 63
8 + 90 = 98
6 + 40 = 46

Page 28 • Subtracting from multiples of ten

1. 10 – 6 = 4
2. 20 – 6 = 14
3. 30 – 6 = 24
4. 40 – 6 = 34
5. 50 – 6 = 44
6. 60 – 6 = 54
7. 70 – 6 = 64
8. 80 – 6 = 74
9. 90 – 6 = 84
10. 100 – 6 = 94
11. 10 – 2 = 8
12. 20 – 2 = 18
13. 30 – 2 = 28
14. 40 – 2 = 38
15. 50 – 2 = 48
16. 60 – 2 = 58
17. 70 – 2 = 68
18. 80 – 2 = 78
19. 90 – 2 = 88
20. 100 – 2 = 98

Brodie's Fast Five

10 – 4 = 6
10 – 9 = 1
10 – 5 = 5
10 – 3 = 7
10 – 8 = 2

Page 29 • Let's make twenty

0 + 20
20 + 0
1 + 19
19 + 1
2 + 18
18 + 2
3 + 17
17 + 3
4 + 16
16 + 4
5 + 15
15 + 5
6 + 14
14 + 6
7 + 13
13 + 7
8 + 12
12 + 8
9 + 11
11 + 9
10 + 10

0 + 20 = 20
20 + 0 = 20
1 + 19 = 20
19 + 1 = 20
2 + 18 = 20
18 + 2 = 20
3 + 17 = 20
17 + 3 = 20
4 + 16 = 20
16 + 4 = 20
5 + 15 = 20
15 + 5 = 20
6 + 14 = 20
14 + 6 = 20
7 + 13 = 20
13 + 7 = 20
8 + 12 = 20
12 + 8 = 20
9 + 11 = 20
11 + 9 = 20
10 + 10 = 20

Brodie's Fast Five

6 + 14 = 20
7 + 13 = 20
12 + 8 = 20
13 + 7 = 20
9 + 11 = 20

Page 30 • Let's make eleven

21 – 10
20 – 9
19 – 8
18 – 7
17 – 6
16 – 5
15 – 4
14 – 3
13 – 2
12 – 1
11 – 0

21 – 10 = 11
20 – 9 = 11
19 – 8 = 11
18 – 7 = 11
17 – 6 = 11
16 – 5 = 11
15 – 4 = 11
14 – 3 = 11
13 – 2 = 11
12 – 1 = 11
11 – 0 = 11

Brodie's Fast Five

20 – 9 = 11
17 – 6 = 11
13 – 2 = 11
19 – 8 = 11
22 – 11 = 11

Page 31 • Addition and subtraction

1. Additions:
   5 + 15 = 20   15 + 5 = 20
   Subtractions:
   20 – 15 = 5   20 – 5 = 15
2. Additions:
   7 + 8 = 15   8 + 7 = 15
   Subtractions:
   15 – 7 = 8   15 – 8 = 7

Brodie's Fast Five

64 – 4 = 60
83 – 3 = 80
92 – 2 = 90
76 – 70 = 6
95 – 90 = 5

Page 32 • Progress Test 5

1. 10 – 5 = 5
2. 20 – 5 = 15
3. 30 – 5 = 25
4. 40 – 5 = 35
5. 50 – 5 = 45
6. 60 – 5 = 55
7. 70 – 5 = 65
8. 80 – 5 = 75
9. 90 – 5 = 85
10. 100 – 5 = 95
11. 10 – 3 = 7
12. 20 – 3 = 17
13. 30 – 3 = 27
14. 40 – 3 = 37
15. 50 – 3 = 47
16. 60 – 3 = 57
17. 70 – 3 = 67
18. 80 – 3 = 77
19. 90 – 3 = 87
20. 100 – 3 = 97
21. Additions:
    6 + 13 = 19   13 + 6 = 19
    Subtractions:
    19 – 13 = 6   19 – 6 = 13
22. Additions:
    8 + 5 = 13   5 + 8 = 13
    Subtractions:
    13 – 5 = 8   13 – 8 = 5

Page 33 • Adding two-digit numbers and units

Set A
1. $26 + 3 = 29$
2. $44 + 4 = 48$
3. $52 + 7 = 59$
4. $31 + 9 = 40$
5. $76 + 5 = 81$
6. $84 + 3 = 87$
7. $67 + 4 = 71$
8. $92 + 7 = 99$
9. $65 + 7 = 72$
10. $88 + 5 = 93$

Set B
1. $35 + 7 = 42$
2. $89 + 9 = 98$
3. $63 + 7 = 70$
4. $58 + 6 = 64$
5. $34 + 7 = 41$
6. $47 + 6 = 53$
7. $59 + 6 = 65$
8. $28 + 8 = 36$
9. $33 + 4 = 37$
10. $94 + 9 = 103$

Brodie's Fast Five

$7 + 32 = 39$
$42 + 5 = 47$
$4 + 52 = 56$
$63 + 9 = 72$
$6 + 82 = 88$

Page 34 • Subtracting units from two-digit numbers

Set A
1. $39 - 6 = 33$
2. $58 - 7 = 51$
3. $79 - 3 = 76$
4. $99 - 4 = 95$
5. $67 - 5 = 62$
6. $48 - 7 = 41$
7. $56 - 6 = 50$
8. $85 - 8 = 77$
9. $92 - 5 = 87$
10. $74 - 6 = 68$

Set B
11. $68 - 2 = 66$
12. $37 - 2 = 35$
13. $42 - 2 = 40$
14. $75 - 2 = 73$
15. $91 - 2 = 89$
16. $53 - 2 = 51$
17. $84 - 2 = 82$
18. $55 - 2 = 53$
19. $95 - 2 = 93$
20. $23 - 2 = 21$

Brodie's Fast Five

$69 - 7 = 62$
$47 - 4 = 43$
$88 - 4 = 84$
$52 - 5 = 47$
$91 - 6 = 85$

Page 35 • Adding two-digit numbers and tens

Set A
1. $26 + 40 = 66$
2. $44 + 30 = 74$
3. $52 + 20 = 72$
4. $37 + 50 = 87$
5. $48 + 30 = 78$
6. $25 + 70 = 95$
7. $18 + 80 = 98$
8. $32 + 60 = 92$
9. $21 + 60 = 81$
10. $38 + 40 = 78$

Set B
1. $20 + 78 = 98$
2. $50 + 49 = 99$
3. $60 + 27 = 87$
4. $30 + 46 = 76$
5. $70 + 17 = 87$
6. $40 + 23 = 63$
7. $50 + 32 = 82$
8. $80 + 28 = 108$
9. $70 + 36 = 106$
10. $90 + 15 = 105$

Brodie's Fast Five

$27 + 40 = 67$
$29 + 30 = 59$
$43 + 50 = 93$
$40 + 39 = 79$
$61 + 20 = 81$

Page 36 • Subtracting two-digit numbers and tens

1. $87 - 20 = 67$
2. $93 - 40 = 53$
3. $76 - 50 = 26$
4. $34 - 20 = 14$
5. $59 - 30 = 29$
6. $72 - 40 = 32$
7. $95 - 60 = 35$
8. $48 - 20 = 28$
9. $61 - 30 = 31$
10. $38 - 10 = 28$
11. $90 - 24 = 66$
12. $40 - 17 = 23$
13. $80 - 53 = 27$
14. $60 - 19 = 41$
15. $30 - 18 = 12$
16. $70 - 47 = 23$
17. $90 - 45 = 45$
18. $100 - 33 = 67$
19. $80 - 39 = 41$
20. $60 - 42 = 18$

Brodie's Fast Five

$49 - 30 = 19$
$99 - 40 = 59$
$83 - 30 = 53$
$50 - 42 = 8$
$100 - 19 = 81$

Page 37 • Addition and subtraction

1. Additions:
   $36 + 24 = 60$ $24 + 36 = 60$
   Subtractions:
   $60 - 36 = 24$ $60 - 24 = 36$
2. Additions:
   $48 + 32 = 80$ $32 + 48 = 80$
   Subtractions:
   $80 - 48 = 32$ $80 - 32 = 48$

Brodie's Fast Five

$64 - 40 = 24$
$87 - 30 = 57$
$92 - 20 = 72$
$76 - 50 = 26$
$95 - 60 = 35$

Page 38 • Progress Test 6

1. $34 + 3 = 37$
2. $53 + 4 = 57$
3. $81 + 7 = 88$
4. $51 + 9 = 60$
5. $88 + 5 = 93$
6. $59 - 7 = 52$
7. $76 - 6 = 70$
8. $93 - 8 = 85$
9. $51 - 5 = 46$
10. $34 - 6 = 28$
11. $20 + 47 = 67$
12. $50 + 32 = 82$
13. $60 + 39 = 99$
14. $30 + 56 = 86$
15. $70 + 23 = 93$
16. $82 - 30 = 52$
17. $76 - 40 = 36$
18. $90 - 33 = 57$
19. $50 - 29 = 21$
20. $60 - 17 = 43$
21. Additions:
    $23 + 37 = 60$ $37 + 23 = 60$
    Subtractions:
    $60 - 37 = 23$ $60 - 23 = 37$
22. Additions:
    $46 + 24 = 70$ $24 + 46 = 70$
    Subtractions:
    $70 - 46 = 24$ $70 - 24 = 46$

Page 40 • Addition in columns

1. $52 + 26 = 78$
2. $63 + 14 = 77$
3. $34 + 25 = 59$
4. $46 + 31 = 77$
5. $58 + 31 = 89$
6. $67 + 25 = 92$
7. $49 + 35 = 84$
8. $38 + 38 = 76$
9. $69 + 27 = 96$
10. $45 + 45 = 90$

Brodie's Fast Five

$46 + 3 = 49$
$46 + 13 = 59$
$46 + 23 = 69$
$46 + 33 = 79$
$46 + 43 = 89$

Page 42 • Subtraction in columns

1. $68 - 35 = 33$
2. $79 - 42 = 37$
3. $97 - 56 = 41$
4. $84 - 21 = 63$
5. $56 - 34 = 22$
6. $72 - 47 = 25$
7. $81 - 58 = 23$
8. $93 - 38 = 55$
9. $80 - 32 = 48$
10. $96 - 44 = 52$

Brodie's Fast Five

$69 - 2 = 67$
$69 - 12 = 57$
$69 - 22 = 47$
$69 - 32 = 37$
$69 - 42 = 27$

Page 43 • Addition and subtraction

1. $48 - 25 = 23$
2. $34 + 25 = 59$
3. $79 - 34 = 45$
4. $43 + 36 = 79$
5. $52 - 36 = 16$
6. $58 + 36 = 94$
7. $61 - 29 = 32$
8. $56 + 29 = 85$
9. $80 - 36 = 44$
10. $67 + 33 = 100$

Brodie's Fast Five

$57 - 3 = 54$
$57 - 13 = 44$
$57 - 23 = 34$
$57 - 33 = 24$
$57 - 43 = 14$

Page 44 • Progress Test 7

1. $84 - 37 = 47$
2. $67 + 29 = 96$
3. $72 - 48 = 24$
4. $42 + 36 = 78$
5. $80 - 36 = 44$
6. $37 + 37 = 74$
7. $99 - 54 = 45$
8. $58 + 37 = 95$
9. $90 - 45 = 45$
10. $71 + 29 = 100$
11. $100 - 69 = 31$
    $82 - 46 = 36$
    $101 - 57 = 44$
    $100 - 31 = 69$
    $82 - 36 = 46$
    $101 - 44 = 57$